A NOTE OF WELCOME

Hello. You are about to take pot luck with Pogo, which is, of course, a little like finding pieces of eight in your morning cereal. (This book happens to be a piece of eight, being the eighth Pogo book.) If you *did* find pieces of eight in your morning cereal, it would be pretty sleazy of you to sue the cereal company for choking on them. Likewise, we can entertain no complaints about any choking induced by laughter while reading Pot Luck Pogo. You have been warned.   SIMON AND SCHUSTER

Other Books by Walt Kelly

NEW YORK

POTLUCK POGO

by
Walt Kelly

SIMON AND SCHUSTER

CONTENTS

LINES UPON A TRANQUIL BROW

HAVE YOU EVER,
WHILE PONDERING THE WAYS OF THE MORN,
THOUGHT TO SAVE JUST A BIT,
JUST A DROP IN THE HORN,
TO POUR IN THE EVENING OR LATE AFTERNOON
OR DURING THE NIGHT WHEN WE'RE
SHINING THE MOON?
HAVE YOU EVER CRIED OUT,
WHILE COUNTING THE SNOW,
OR WATCHING THE TOMTIT WARBLE
HELLO...
"BREAK OUT THE CIGARS, THIS LIFE
IS FOR SQUIRRELS;
WE'RE OFF TO THE DRUGSTORE
TO WHISTLE AT GIRLS"

?

Chapter *1*

BRISKLY BREATHING

Wherein our men
make a running start
at a dead end.

2

LEMME TELL YOU MY KIND OF A JOKE··· SEEMS A MAN WAS TALKIN' TO A MOTH 'BOUT **TAX PROBLEMS**···THE MOTH SAYS: "THEM TAXES HITS ME RIGHT WHERE I LIVE·····*IN YOUR POCKETBOOK!*"

OL' FRANK SIDEBOTHAM

STOP SNORIN'!

OL' FRANK SIDEBOTHAM

HEY! POGO!

HEY!

MISTER FRANK

REMEMBER NOW···A MAN TALKIN' TO A MOTH 'BOUT TAXES···OL' MOTH SAY: "THEM TAXES HITS ME RIGHT WHERE I LIVE··· *IN YOUR POCKETBOOK!*" ···GO AHEAD··· TELL IT TO POGO.

CHURCHY TOLE ME A SCREAMER···A MAN SEE A MOTH AN' HE SAY TAXES IS HITTIN' ME RIGHT IN THE POCKETBOOK AND THE MOTH SAID I···UH···UM···UG··· ···LESSEE···I FERGIT WHAT THE MOTH SAY.

THAT'S PERTY GOOD! IMAGINE···A MAN CARRYIN' ON A CONVERSATION WITH A MOTH··

YEAH!

YEAH, I THUNK IT WAS FUNNY TOO··· ···YOU HAD ANY LUCK? US CAUGHT NARY A MINNIE··

PSSST! HEY! PSSST!

YUP···GIT OL' CHURCHY···US'LL GO HOME AN' HAVE A FRY.

DID HE TELL ABOUT THE *MOTH?*

THE ONE GOT HIT WITH A *POCKETBOOK?*

DOWN!

Chapter 2

BRACKISH BRINE

"I can handle my dukes
but somebody keep an eye
on the duchess."

7

NOW--! LOOK! LOOK! HE'S FIGHTIN' FOUL ALREADY ---GIVE A LOOK, POGO! SEE! HE'S *UNFAIR!*

WELL-- UH- HUH HUM-SAY-- WELL, NOW.

IT'S HARD TO B'LEEVE YOU KNOWS MUCH ABOUT JUDO IF YOU LET THAT *WORM* CHILE THROW YOU.

A ACCIDENT.

BUT HOW 'BOUT WHEN YOU MISTOOK MY **TAIL** FOR A WORM ---CERT'LY YOU KNOWS MORE JUDO THAN MY *TAIL* DOES.

WHO'S TO SAY HOW MUCH YO' TAIL KNOWS?

SHUCKS -- I OUGHT TO KNOW ---IT'S **MY** TAIL.

I KNOW-- I KNOW-- BUT WE GET OUT OF TOUCH WITH THESE THINGS.

HOW KIN A MAN GIT OUT OF TOUCH WITH HIS OWN TAIL?

OH, AS YEARS GO BY YOU GROWS AWAY FROM EACH OTHER.

9

Chapter *3*

BRAZENLY WE BRAY

A secret should be seen
and not heard.

11

I IS WILLIN' TO LISTEN...WILLIN' TO LET THE BOY *UN*-BURDLE HISSELF ....*BUT YOU*, HA!.... *YOU* WANTS HIM TO KEEP A SECRET LOCKED IN HIS *BOOZIM*... UN-HEARD AN' UN-SUNG.

I WA'N'T FIGGERIN' ON SINGIN' IT.

S'POSE HE *DO* KEEP QUIET... HOW'S HE KNOW IT'S A *BONA-FIDE* SECRET?- ALL THE WORL' MIGHT KNOW *!. TEST IT! TELL IT!* IF FOLKS IS SHOCKED OR SICKENED, HE'LL *KNOW* IT WAS A SECRET

IT'S THE ONLY WAY.

POGO, LOOK AT IT THE *HUMANE* WAY--- MOUSE CAN'T KEEP HIS SECRET LOCKED UP *FOR*-EVER. IF HE GONE TELL, *LET HIM TOLE IT TO INTELLIGIBOBBLE FOLKS LIKE US'NS.*

RIGHT! I IS READY.

HERE I GO... NOW, LISTEN CLOSE...

STOP!

WHUFFO *STOP.!?.* HOW COME THIS *HITEY-MITEY* AIR? WHAT KIND OF A *ATT*-ITUDE'S YOU CALL THAT?

ADAMANT!

BY JING, MR. MOUSE, IF HE GONE CUSS AN' CARRY ON, US'LL TAKE OUR SECRET ELSEWHERE.

'LONG AS HE SUCH A *FUSS BUDGET* 'BOUT THIS SECRET (NOT WANTIN' TO *HEAR* IT AN' ALL), TELL IT PRIVATE...... *OUTEN HIS EARSHOTS*..

RIGHT

HOLE ON! STOP!

A *FINE THING!* WE GOES OFF AWAY FROM YOU SO'S NOT TO INFRINGE YO' *SCRUPLES* 'GAINST LISTENIN' TO SECRETS AN' *STILL* YOU PREVENTS OL' MOUSE FROM TELLIN'.... YOU GOT ANYTHIN' TO SAY FOR YO'SELF?

YEAH.... WAIT FOR ME...

LISTEN CLOSE WHILST I WHISPER MY SECRET---

A·HEM......

13

Chapter 4

SIMMERING SONGS

We learn that nothing
helps keep a secret
like being stuck with a bad memory.

I BETCHA A MILLION DOLLARS NOBODY KIN GUESS FOR EXAMPLE THE SECRET I KNOWS ABOUT THE DEACON.

BETCHA A BILLION I KIN.

BETCHA A TRILLION.

BETCHA A DOUBLE TRILLION -- A TRIPLE TRILLION!

BETCHA ALL THE MONEY IN FORT KNOX.

AIN'T NOBODY GONNA LISTEN TO MY SECRET!?

I BET ALL THE MONEY IN THE WORLD!

I BET ALL THE MONEY IN THE UNIVERSE.

WHY DO YOU GOTTA SO CRUDELY BREAK INON A INTELLECTUAL DISCUSSION?

I DOUBLE THAT!

I TRIPLE IT!

OL' MOUSE IS STILL WAITIN' TO TELL HIS SECRET-- WHILST YOU TWO ARGUES, HOW 'BOUT HIM TELLIN'?

IT MOUGHT RELIEVE THE SITUATION AT THAT.

LEASTWISE IT'LL SAVE MY CARAMEL CANDIES WHAT HE BEEN EATIN'-- OKAY, MOUSE-- NOW'S YO' CHANCE.

OKAY.. NOW'S YO' CHANCE.

IMAGINE THAT? HE WAITS TWO WEEKS TO TELL A STORY. THEN WHEN HE GIT THE GO-AHEAD HE LOSE HIS HEARIN'-- STAN' BACK WHILST I BLAST A..

TAIN'T HIS EARS! HIS JAW BONES IS STUCK TOGETHER BY THEM CANDIES.

MY SAKES! THIS IS A DESPERMINT SITUATION-- HOW WE GONE FIND THE SECRET IF MOUSE'S JAWS IS LOCKED SHUT BY CANDY?

UNTIL HE COULDN'T TALK NOBODY WAS GIVIN' HIM A EAR ATALL.

'AT'S WHAT HE GIT FOR BEIN' A PIG-- HIS JAW-BONES GOT GUMMED UP BY HIM EATIN' ALL THESE CARAMELS.

IFFEN HE CAN'T PRY 'EM LOOSE, IT'S A LUCKY THING I IS HERE 'CAUSE I KNOWS HOW TO UN-STUCK HIS TEETHS-- YOU JES' TAKE - A - GUNK -- UH-- UNG

YES-YES! GO ON!

18

Chapter 5

OF SWIMMING SWINE

A lateral translation
proves to be
a very forward pass.

HERE'S GRUNDOON ALL READY TO GO ON OVER AN' *TRANSLATE* OL' MOUSE'S TALK.

GOOD! I SEE HE IS PACKED A NICE LI'L' LUNCH...

YEPSIRREE... AN' HE INSIST ON DOIN' IT HIS OWN SELF... AW, LOOKY HOW SOFT HE BITES ME GOODBYE...

A *FORE-THOUGHTED* CHILE...HM, GOT A NICE HEFT ON HER, TOO ♩ ♪

I'LL JES' CARRY THIS FOR THE TAD AN' UM...MM 5♭ DM ♩ TIDDLE-DUM ♩♪ OH HUMM ♩

HM♩ DM ♩♪ M TIDDLE ♩ DEE ♩ HM - DM - UNG.. MPH ...HMMMMM

DIN'T *NO-BODY* NEVER TOLE YOU *MUD-PIES* AIN'T ACTUAL NO LEGAL LUNCH!?

HERE'S OL' *GRUNDOON* WHAT TALKS LIKE OL' MOUSE WITH HIS JAWS STUCK ---*HE* KNOWS A *NEW WORD*.

GMX!

ALL SET TO *TRANSLATE*, I HOPES.

MDXTNGR BPTFRD GBNNTZ?

SMPPR NBS GBTN XZGR PTS!

WHAT'D HE SAY? WHAT'D HE SAY?

SMPPR NBS GBTN XZGR PTS!

PTS!

OH, WELL, US FERGOT WE DON'T UNDERSTAN' GRUNDOON NEITHER... 'LESS'N MEBBE HE COULD USE HIS NEW WORD ..... WHAT WAS IT?

BYE-BYE

'TAIN'T MUCH HELP...'LESS SOMEBODY GONNA SHOVE OFF.

ZNX BYE BYE ZPTX.

?

GIVE IT ONE MORE TRY, MOUSE; TALK SOME MORE WITH YOUR JAWS STUCK SHUT BY CANDY AN' SEE KIN THE TAD TRANSLATE ....

MEBBE GRUNDOON'LL GIT A CHANCT TO USE HIS NEW WORD...

GNBTS

MSB GMBBRTZ PTFRK NSTLSKL NSBVRD MNPQR TVWXZ!

DON'T FORGIT TO USE YOUR NEW WORD, SON....

BYE-BYE, BYE-BYE, BYE-BYE, BYE-BYE, BYE-BYE, BYE-BYE, BYE-BYE, BYE-BYE, BYE-BYE, BYE-BYE, BYE-BYE ....

HIS NEW WORD

HEY! COME BACK!

WE HEARD WHAT THE BOY SAID... IF YOU WANTS TO LISTEN TO ANOTHER HOUR OF BYE-BYE OKAY, BUT BYE-BYE

22

GREAT... THEY IS OPEN.. OPEN AT LAST---NOW, TELL ME THE SECRET YOU BEEN DYIN' TO TELL ME..

I - UH *FERGITS*

WHY, YOU UNGRATEFUL *INGRATE!* AFTER ALL MY WORK...! I THOUGHT YOU WAS *DYIN'* TO TELL...

OOG... YOU AIN'T *FOOLIN'!*

I'VE A *GOOD* MIND TO *NEVER* SPEAK TO YOU AGAIN---

I'M GLAD YOU GOT A GOOD MIND FOR *SOMETHIN'*..YOU ALMOS' SHOOK ME LOOSE FROM MY CHASSIS GITTIN' MY *JAWBONES* UNSTUCK...

FOR *WEEKS* YOU WAS *BIG BRAGGIN'* 'BOUT THIS *HOT TIME* SECRET YOU WAS GONE TELL --- THEN YOU GOT YOUR JAWS STUCK ---AN' WHEN WE OPENS 'EM.

YEAH...I FORGOT THE SECRET.

Chapter 6

SCATTERING SATURDAY

Kansas corn:

A tall story in short.

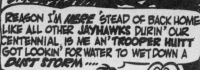

REASON I'M *HERE* 'STEAD OF BACK HOME LIKE ALL OTHER *JAYHAWKS* DURIN' OUR CENTENNIAL IS ME AN' *TROOPER HUTT* GOT LOOKIN' FOR WATER TO WET DOWN A *DUST STORM*....

WE DRUV CROST THE *KAW*, LOOKED THE REPUBLICAN RIVER OVER.... NARY A DROP.... COME TO A BIG HILL ON THE OUTSKIRTS OF *TOPEKA*, (PLACE CALLED *WICHITA*), SO OL' LYLE PUT THE CAR INTO LOW....

WE *CLUMB* AND WE *CLUMB* FOR HALF A DAY; GOT TO THE TOP AN' LYLE SAYS: *MAN, WE'RE OUT OF GAS!*.. SO HE STARTS WALKIN' BACK DOWN... NO SOONER'S HE OUT OF SIGHT THAN THINGS START MOVIN'...

THAT DAG BONED HILL WAS A *DUST CLOUD FORTY MILE HIGH* BEIN' BLOWED EAST CROST THE STATE LINE AN' THRU *MISSOURI*... ...AN' ME STUCK ON TOP WITH A *HOT PATROL CAR* AN' *NO GAS!*

WHOOIE!

I TRIED TO STEER THIS KANSAS *DUST CLOUD* I WAS RIDIN' ON TOWARD WASHINGTON TO LET 'EM SEE WHAT A REAL DUST STORM LOOKS LIKE... THEN *I* SAYS *NOBODY* ON *CAPITOL HILL* WILL KNOW THE DIFFER'NCE....

ON ACCOUNT OF THIS IS THE *WINDY* SEASON UP THERE, TOO.... ANYWAY, THE CLOUD WAS HEADIN' SOUTH-EAST, SO I WRIT A LETTER TO THE *EDITOR*, TO OL' *TOM KIENE*...

25

BACK AT THE STATE JOURNAL... I SAYS: TOM, US JAYHAWKS DON'T MIND SHARIN' OUR GOOD STATE WITH THE UNDERPRIVILEGED, *BUT*, TAKIN' A LOOK AT THIS BITE I'M ON, MEBBE IT'D BE A GOOD IDEA...

IF THE REST OF THE *U.S. AND A.* WOULD GIVE US BACK THE *CHAW* AND TAKE THE *PLUG* ....WELL, SIR, I FOUND A POST OFFICE, BUILT ON THAT DUST CLOUD BY A ABSENT-MINDED *ADMINISTRATION*—AN' SO I.........

AFTER MAILIN' THE LETTER TO THE TOPEKA STATE JOURNAL UP ON THAT DUST CLOUD, I DUG A HOLE AN' SHOVED THE PATROL CAR INTO IT FOR *SAFE KEEPIN'*....

UNFORTUNATELY, THE MACHINE FELL ALL THE WAY *THRU*, WAS SPOTTED BY AN ALERT LAD, BY NAME, ASHMORE, OVER *LITTLE ROCK*... THE PAPER THERE CARRIED A STORY ABOUT A FLYIN' SAUCER NEXT DAY....

THE NYLE MILLER

FINELY, THE DUST CLOUD SETTLED ON THE BANKS OF THE *CHATTA-HOOCHEE* WHERE I HAD IT CUT UP AND SOLD FOR *COFFEE*...TO MY SURPRISE THE ALABAMA POLICE TOOK AFTER ME WITH FERRETS AND RIFLES....

THE NYLE

SEEMS I'D GROUND UP THE *HOLE* TOO, CHARGIN' $1.25 PER POUND, (AN OVERSIGHT) *SO*, I NIPPED INTO *GEORGIA* DISGUISED AS A *RED HEADED WOOD-PECKER*... HA! ME, A JAYHAWK ...AN' A BLOND AT THAT...

WHEN I GOT A JOB WITH THE *HARE* HERE DOIN' *WOOD PECKIN'*, THE CONSTANT *RAPPIN'* ON TREES SHOOK UP MY BRAINS SO I'D OF MADE A *RATTLIN'* GOOD *CONG-ESSMAN*....

I GOT THINKIN': *UNLESS* SOME-THIN'S DONE 'BOUT THE *DUST* THE *WHEAT FIELDS'LL* BE BUT A *BIG HOLE* GOIN' ALL THE WAY THRU TO THE *PACIFIC OCEAN*... THEN, WHEN WE SET OFF A CLUTCH OF *H-BOMBS* OUT THERE .....

..WE'LL BLOW *FORTY-NINE BILLION TONS* OF UNDER-SEA LIFE BACK UP THE HOLE AN' EVERY MAN WEST OF THE MISSISSIPPI WILL BE UP TO HIS ANCESTORS IN *RADIOACTIVE HADDOCK*.... SOME OF 'EM UNDOUBTEDLY *SUBVERSIVE*....

YOU FERGITS THE *McCARRAN ACT*...

THEY'D NEVER GIT PAST THE IMMIGRATION AUTHORITIES...

HEY! DID YOU VARMINTS KETCH ANYTHIN' FOR SUPPER YET?

KIRKE MECHEM

GOLLY, ALBERT, I IS *GLAD* YOU GOT YO' *TEETH UNSTUCK!* WE AIN'T BEEN FISHIN'..... JES' LIST'NIN' TO THE *JAYHAWK*

PHOOMP! WHAT'S THAT KANSAS CRITTUR GOT TO SAY?

HE TELLIN' HOW HE WAS BRUNG UP WHEN A CHILE BY A TRIBE OF *INVISIBLE INDIANS* NORTH OF THE KAW.

INVISIBLE INDIANS! HA! KIN HE *PROVE* THAT?!

NATURALLY..... *BEIN' INVISIBLE THEY NATURAL DIN'T LEAVE NO TRACES AN'; TO THIS DAY, NO SIGN OF 'EM IS EVER BEEN FOUND....* SHEER PROOF!

SHEER.

DUNNO WHY I SHOULD WASTE *MY* TIME TALKIN' TO A *BIRD,* AN' A *MYTHOLOGICAL BEAST* AT THAT. *WHO* EVER HEARD OF A JAY-HAWK RAISED BY *INVISIBLE INDIANS?*

I GOT THE *FEATHERS* TO *PROVE* IT...

THE HON. D. SCHULTZ

THING I LIKED 'BOUT THE SWAMP UP TO NOW WAS THE *DEARTH OF JAYHAWKS.*

WE HAD A PLAGUE OF *ALLIGATOR* ROUND TOPEKA ONCE...

PLAGUE! HMP! PROB'LY TWO SALA-MANDERS AN' A HOPPY TOAD....

NAWP... MILLIONS OF ALLIGATORS.. ONLY OLD PAT DEVLIN PIPED 'EM OUT.

WITH A *TUNE...* LIKE THE PIED PIPER?

*NAWP...*ALLIGATORS BE TONE DEAF. SO PAT PIPED 'EM OUT THRU THE *NATURAL GAS PIPE LINE* ---- FOLKS IN OSH KOSH THO'T THEY WAS *ELEPHANTS,* PUT BUCKLES ON 'EM AN' STARTED THE TRUNK INDUSTRY....

Chapter 7

HEARTS ARE HEAVY

An octopus is
an eight-handed game
of solitaire.

SOMEHOW IT GOT *MIGHTY DARK* ALL OF A SUDDEN.

THAT'S BECAUSE SOMEBODY DUMPED A *CAN OF BAIT* ON YOUR HEAD, MOUSE.

HEY, OL' *SNAVELY!* DOGGONE, I SEE YOU *PEERIN'.*

LOOKS PERTY *COOL* AN' *COZY* IN THERE, SO-- MIND IF I JOIN YOU?

STOP PUSHIN', SNAVELY-- AIN'T HARDLY ROOM FOR TWO-- AN' BESIDES, EVEN THO *I'M YOUR BEST FRIEND* --- I *GOTTA* TELL YOU SOMETHIN' ---

WHAT?

YOU NEEDS A SHAVE.

THOUGHT YOU SAID *ALL* THEM *ELEPHUMPS* HAD AT LEAST FOUR LEGS, FATHER.

HERMES, THEY IS *UNRELIABLE* EARLY IN THE SEASON-BESIDES THAT'S A *SMALL* ONE.

BY JING, *SNAVELY,* IT'S GOOD TO SEE YOU AGAIN --- DID YOU EVER GIT THAT *LI'L WORM* TRAINED TO BE A *FULL FLEDGED SNAKE?*

YOU MEAN THE APPRENTICE COBRA? -- NO, BEIN' A ANGLE WORM HE FIGGERED THE BEST ANGLE WAS TO REMAIN A WORM ---

TOOK A JOB WITH A *OCTOPUS* FAMILY LAST WINTER TUTORING THE SCION OF THE FAMILY-- -- HE HAD A IDEA HE WANTED TO BE A *BOA CONSTRICTOR.*

31

I CONVINCED HIM FINALLY THAT HE WOULD MAKE *SEVEN* BOA CONSTRICTORS WITH ONE ARM TIED BEHIND HIS BACK—

HE TOOK UP MUSIC INSTEAD --- BOUGHT *FOUR VIOLINS* AND STARTED A HOT STRING QUARTET- *HOWEVER*, HE WAS BOOKED INTO CLEVELAND, GOT ALL FOUR INSTRUMENTS GOIN' AN' NATURALLY THIS DIDN'T LEAVE HIM NO LEG TO STAND ON-- SO THE ACT FELL FLAT ON ITS OCTAMETER.

IT'D BE NICE, POGO, IF US JAY HAWKS COULD GIT *I*-DENT-IFIED--

SO'S YOU COULD BE ADMITTED TO THE LODGE?

WELL, SHO'NUFF-- HOW'D *YOU* LIKE TO BE A BIRD, THE ONLY ONE ABLE TO FLY THE *AUSTRALIAN CRAWL* AN' *NO*BODY RECOGNIZES YOU?

GUESS IT *WOULDN'T* PAY--- *I'D* TURN IN MY FEATHERS.

*HOW*EVER IF *I* SAW A BIRD *FLYIN'* THE *AUSTRALIAN CRAWL* I WOULDN'T RECOGNIZE IT SO GOOD EITHER --- HOW'S YOU *DO* THAT?

EASY--BEIN' AS AUSTRALY IS *DOWN UNDER*--

YOU JES' GITS *DOWN* AN' CRAWLS *UNDER* GROUND--- USIN' A OVER ARM CREEP AN' A LOT OF LEG KICKIN'--- OFTEN YOU FLIES FIVE OR SIX FEET DEEP.

NEXT THIS OCTOPUS LEARNED *FOUR HANDED SOLITAIRE* BUT HIS *EAST* CHEATED HIS *WEST* AN' NEVER THE TWAIN SPOKE NO MORE.

THEM ORNERY-THOLOGISTS OUGHT TO BE PUT OUTEN THE *BIRD BUSINESS*---

JES' 'CAUSE THEY DON'T RECOGNIZE YOU, JAY HAWK?

NOBODY RECOGNIZES ME---MAYBE IT'S THE WAY I CUT MY HAIR---

BY MY *SWORD!* A ACTUAL NATURAL BORN REAL LIVE *JAY*---

YES YES? YES YES? *YES?* JAY--?

--*BIRD!*

SEE THAT!? SEE THAT!? THE *FIRST BIRD WATCHER* IN *NINETEEN YEARS* TO SPOT ME CALLS ME A *JAYBIRD!*---A *JAY BIRD*---HOW SHARPER THAN A CHILD'S TOOTH ETC.

HE'S A JAYHAWK -*HAWK*- *HAWK HAWK!*

YOU GOT A BAD THROAT THERE, POSSUM.

SORRY, JAY HAWK, THAT I CALLED YOU A *JAYBIRD*- USED TO BE A MYTHOLOGICAL BEAST MYSELF AN' I KNOWS HOW YOU FEELS.

WAS YOU A *BIRD SPOTTER?*

NO, BUT I WAS A *PLANE* SPOTTER ONCE--USED TO SPOT *JENNIES* FOR THE FEDERABLE GUMMINT--*HOWEVER*, THE *PAINT FUMES* MADE ME GIDDY, AN' IN MY EXUBERANCE--

I SPOTTED THE **COMMODORE** IN CHARGE OF THE PROJECT--QUITE HAN'SOMELY TOO, TO MY MIND, BUT HE CLAIMED HE LOOKED LIKE A **LEOPARD**, A CONDITION NOT TO HIS TASTE, AND SO TORE MY CHEVRONS FROM MY EPAULETS.

BROKEN HEARTED, I BECAME AN **ITINERANT SERPENT**--TOOK A JOB AS AN HOOP SNAKE IN **SALT LAKE CITY** BUT THE AUTHORITIES CLAIMED I WAS A **LEGENDARY MONSTER** AN' I WAS RULED OFF THE TURF-- WHAT THERE WAS **OF** IT OF COURSE.

NEXT I·

BEFORE YOU GOES AHEAD WITH YO' AUTOBIOGRAFTY WHAT HAPPENED TO THAT **OCTOPUS**?

OCTOPUS!? **WHAT** OCTOPUS?

THE ONE YOU TUTORED.

OH **HIM!** WELL, HE GAVE UP PLAYIN' THE VIOLINS AS I SAID AN' HIS PATER AND MATER (GOOD OCTOPODES BOTH) BOUGHT HIM A **BAGPIPE** THINKIN' WHAT WITH ALL HIS UNEMPLOYED ARMS AND SO ON HE COULD · HANDLE THE MACHINE.

HOWEVER, THE LAD TOOK ONE LOOK AT THIS INSTRUMENT AND FELL **MADLY** IN LOVE--SAID IT WAS THE **FIRST PLAID OCTOPUS** HE HAD **EVER** SEEN AND OFFERED HIS EIGHT HANDS IN MARRIAGE-- --**NEEDLESS** TO SAY THERE WAS NO REPLY AND SO HE GOT A JOB WAVING GOODBYE ON PIER 42 AN'····

Chapter 8

CLUBS ARE TRUMP

Who put the meter
on the watermelon rhyme?

THEY AIN'T *NOTHIN'* WORSE NOR **UN-IGNITED** LOVE---'CEPT **FRIED PARSNIPS** AN' **CODDLED WATERMILLION.**

ADDLED TURTLE IS EXTREMEFULLY *LOATHFUL* TOO ---

ANY KIND OF COOKED TURTLE UPSET *ME* SOMETHIN' AWFUL. STILL, I FEELS **SORRY** FOR OL' DEACON.

NOW IF YOU WRITES A LOVE BALLAD OR A SONNET FOR OL' DEACON--

I STILL CAN'T BLEEVE HE CARES 'BOUT ME.

HE DON'T! HIM AN' MIZ BOOMBAH IS IN LOVE --- ALL I IS ASKIN' YOU TO DO IS RHYME UP A LI'L **SOMETHIN'** FOR HIM FOR **HER.**

HERE, I'LL GIVE YOU A SAMPLE-- HOW'S YOU SPELL "KISSES"?

WITH A "**X**"---- WUNNER WHY DEACON COOLED OFF ON *ME* ALL OVER SUDDEN?

Dear X: XXXXX XXXXX. *Very truly* X

LAND! SHE'LL NEVER KNOW WHO'S IT **TO**-- NOR WHO'S IT FROM!

YEAH--WELL, FIX **THAT** PART UP. MAKE IT **RHYME,** AN' LET'S **SEND** IT!

37

TROUBLE IS -- IF I WRITES A **STUNNER** OF A POEM FER THE **DEACON** AN' IT OVERCOMES **MIZ BOOMBAH** -- WHO'S SHE GONNA WANNA **MARRY** --?

A **GOOD** QUESTION --

HIM OR **ME**? HIM AS THE **GIVEE** OR ME AS THE **PARTICIPEE**?

LET'S SEE WHAT YOU IS WRIT.

I FIGGER, WITH A **CHORUS OF 100 KATYDIDS** BACKIN' HIM UP IT'D MAKE QUITE A **IMPRESSION**!

"ALL THE WAY FROM MAINE TO TEXAS I COVER YOU WITH ALL TYPES X'S -- GET IN AN' FIGHT, TEAM, **RECKETY REXXES**!"

UNDOUBTALLY SHE'LL MARRY **WHOMSOEVER** IS **INNOCENT.**

YOU SURE **THIS** IS THE BEST POEM YOU KIN WRITE TO **WOO MIZ BOOMBAH** FOR OL' **DEACON**?

YEP.

IT DON'T SEEM IT GOT THE EAR-MARKS OF A **INNERESTED** PARTY -- HOW COME YOU DON'T CARRY ON 'BOUT **MIZ BOOMBAH'S** LOVELY LONG LASHED EYES OF BLUE?

TRUTH TO TELL SHE GOT EYES LIKE **TWO SLICES OF FRIED BANANA!**

WULL---US'LL EACH THINK OF SOMETHIN' NICER LOOKIN' 'BOUT MIZ BOOMBAH THAN HER EYEBALLS THEN--- MM--HM..

I IS, UGH, DOIN' MY BEST.

UH--- MEBBE WE BETTER STICK WITH YO' QUIETLY BEAUTIFUL OBSERVATION THAT SHE GOT EYES LIKE TWO SLICES OF FRIED BANANAS--

LONG AS THE UNINETY FRUIT PEOPLE DON'T MIND--

CHURCHY

I'M GONNA DISGUISE MYSELF LIKE A GOLDY HAIRED CHILE WHEN I DELIVERS DEACON'S POEM TO MIZ BOOMBAH--

WHUFFO? IN THE WORL', WHUFFO?

CHURCHY

SO'S SHE WON'T THINK IT'S ME WHAT IS IN LOVE OF HER --- THE VERSE WE WRIT FOR DEACON IS PERTY DOGBONED OVERPOWERIN'!

"THOU HAS A VOICE LIKE A THROBBIN' TURKLE DOVE, WHILST THEE BLEATETH OUT A SONG OF LOVE! THINE EYES ARE SOFT LIKE SWEET MANANA, SOFT AND GOOEY LIKE FRIED BANANA".

UH, YOU BETTER TAKE THIS LI'L' *IMPLEMENT* ALONG---- MIZ BOOMBAH MOUGHT BE EVEN *MORE OVER-POWERIN'*---

CHURCHY, WHILE YOU DEE-LIVERS *DEACON'S LOVE POEM* TO *MIZ BOOMBAH*, I'LL POP 'ROUN' AN' TELL DEACON WE IS WOOIN' THE GAL FOR HIM.

HE'LL BE *EE-*TERNAL GRATEFUL.

HAW--*DIS*GUISED AS I IS THIS WAY--*NOBODY* WOULDN'T KNOW I WASN'T A GOOD LOOKIN' YALLER HAIRED GAL CRITTUR.

H'LO THERE, CHURCHY LA FEMME.

H'LO.

YO' FRIEND, MR. LA FEMME, LOOK A LI'L' *PEAKIED*, PA---- HE BEEN SICK?

NO--- HE DON'T CHANGE MUCH---

40

41

Chapter 9

DIAMONDS ARE IN ROUGH

A woman's not always a woman
but a good cigar
is a horse of another feather.

IT 'PEARS AS IF OL' **P.T. BRIDGEPORT'S** CIRCUS IS LET LOOSE ONE OF ITS **SIDESHOW ODDITIES.**

UGH.

ONLY THING ABOUT BEIN' MADE UP LIKE A **BEAUTIFUL GAL**, POGO, IT'S KINDA **RISKY.**

WHO CAN TELL WHEN SOME GAY **LOCHINVAR** FROM OUT OF THE WEST MIGHT SWEEP ME OFF MY FEET?---- AN' **ME** SO **YOUNG**--

PSST, POGO-- IF THAT OL' LADY IS **BOTHERIN'** YOU, US'LL GIT A STICK AN' HELP YOU CHASE HER.

HAUGH-**SOME FOLKS** GOT ALL THE **TASTE** AN' **FINER SENSIBILITIES** OF A CAN OF **WARM BAIT.**

THIS AIN'T NO **UGLY OLD LADY**, THIS IS MERE **CHURCHY LA FEMME** IN **DIS**GUISE---

I STILL SAY "UGH."

THERE'S THEM AS SAY I IS PERTY DOGGONE **FETCHIN'** AN' **FASCINATIN'.**

DRESSED LIKE THIS I TAKES AFTER MY **AUNT MOOMIE**-- ONE OF THE RAVISHIN' **BEAUTIES** OF THE **TIDELANDS** IN '96.

I REMEMBER HER NOW; USED TO PLAY **SECOND BASE** FOR THE OLD ORIOLES...

NO--NO-- SHE WAS **LIGHT-WEIGHT CHAMPEEN** OF THE CHESAPEAKE, OL' TERRAPIN McGOVERN.

BY JING! MY AUNT MOOMIE WAS SUCH A LOOKER SHE COULD **OUTSTRIP** ANY **THEATRICYCLE QUEEN** OF **TODAY**!

EVEN WITHOUT THE MODERN ZIPPER?

IF YOU CAN'T ACK LIKE A **GENNLEMAN**, STOP BEIN' **A LADY**!

WE IS PROBBLE BROKE HIS LI'L' GIRL HEART---

DAG NAG IT! I KNOW MY RIGHTS ---I AIN'T GONE STAN' ROUN' AN' LET WOMANHOOD BE **INSULTED**.

I'LL BE **RUMDIDDLED**, OSBERT! THERE SHE IS NOW --- *RUN OVER AN' ASK HER!*

STORY BOOK

HEY! MISS! HEY! HEY! IF YOU'RE **LI'L' RED RIDING HOOD** WHERE'S YOUR **THREE BEARS**?

A SMART YOUNG 'UN IF EVER I SAW ONE.

WAH! SHE SAY SHE'S **GOLDIE LONKS** AN' LOOKIN' FOR HER **LOST SHEEP**.

MADAME, WHY CAN'T YOU **OWN UP**? ADMIT YOU'RE RED RIDING HOOD-- WHY DESTROY A SON'S FAITH IN HIS FATHER?

47

NOW, LET'S SEE--WAS I GONNA GIVE THAT **LOVE** POEM TO DEACON OR MIZ BOOMBAH?

HUM!

OOP! ISN'T YOU **UNCLE BALDWIN?** THE **KISSIN'** UNCLE OF **OL' PORKY-PINE?**

YUP... C'MERE.

NOTHIN' DOIN'!

WHAT'S A MATTER WITH THAT OL' CHURCHY? ALL I WANTED TO DO WAS **STRAIGHTEN HIS WIG.**

BY **JING** AN' BY **GOLLAMICKLE,** THERE'S A **SHO'NUFF BEAUTIFUL GAL** TROMPIN' HER SYLPH-LIKE WAY 'ROUN' THE SWAMP.

HAW! MAN! IT'S A MIRAWOCKLE HOW ALL YOU GALS FALLS FOR ME ---

Chapter *10*

SPADES ARE SPOTTY

Woman has a double clutch
but man must shift for himself.

BY JING! THERE'S THEM GALS HAVIN' TEA---AN' ME WITH MY **SEEGAR**---GOTTA DUCK IT **SOMEWHERES**.

AND SO I SAID TO HIM I SAID, "DEACON," I SAID...

WELL, **HERE** I IS! OL' DEACON SENT ME OVER TO SAY HIS BRAIN IS **A-FLAME**.

HMMPH.

AN'--UH--IT LOOK LIKE HE AIN'T THE **ONLY** ONE--- COULD I BORRY THE LOAN OF A CUP OF TEA?

A PLEASURE.. ONE LUMP OR TWICE?

IT DON'T MATTER---ACTUAL I GOT A SWEET TOOTH FOR **LEMON**.

PERHOP YOU PREFER COFFEE, MAM'SELLE?

HUMPH HUMPH HUMPH HUMPH HUMPH HUMPH HUMPH HUMPH HUMPH **HUMPH!**

YOU CAN SAY **THAT** AGAIN!

52

53

YOU HAVE EATEN THE CAKE OF THE **WOMAN I LOVE**...

GOOD, TOO!

I **ADMIRE** YO' TASTE, SIR-- SHE BAKES A **ROUSER** OF A CAKE.

BUT **THINK** OF THE **WASTE!** THINK OF THE LOVIN' AN' **DEE**-VOTED CARE WHAT WENT INTO THE BAKIN'... **ALL LOST!**

AH, THE **SWEET SACRIFICE** SHE PUT INTO THAT CAKE...**ALL FOR ME**...AN' WHO ATE IT? NOBODY BUT A **UNAPPRECIATIVE, UNCULTURED BOOR** AN' **SLOB** WHAT WAS ALSO A **THIEF** TO BOOT.

YOU CAN'T TALK ABOUT HIM THAT WAY!

I **DOUBLE DAST DARE** YOU TO REPEAT THE **LOUD UNCOUTH REE**-MARK YOU **JES'** MADE.

I SAYS YOU CAN'T CALL MY PAL NO **BOOR** AN' **SLOB**.

HE DIN'T NEVER CALL ME NO SLOB AN' A BOOR! STOP **PROTECTIN'** MY GOOD NAME!

I WILL PROTECT **YOURN!**

AN'. I SAYS YOU CAN'T CALL **MY PAL** NO **BOOR** AN' NO **SLOB!**

YOU'RE **RIGHT**, OWL -- I DIN'T CALL **YOU** A **BOOR** AN' **SLOB**----

YAAAN! **SEE?** ALL I GOTTA **PROTECK** NOW IS **YOUR** GOOD NAME!

NOR DID I CALL **CHURCHY LA FEMME** A BOOR AN' A SLOB---- IN ALL FAIRNESS THE **JUST** AND **FAIR DOG** MUST **SO** RENDER **JUDGEMENT**...

I CALLED YOU BOTH A BOOR AND A SLOB!

THAT'S **ONE** BOOR AN' **ONE** SLOB--- AN' THEY IS **TWO** OF US ...**WHICH IS WHICH?**

DIVIDE IT UP FAIR AN' SQUARE, **ONE APIECE.**

Chapter *11*

JOKERS JUMP

Don't go to a lot of trouble—
we'll bring it to *you*.

How shameful! A strong man bullying a frail and lovely lady~ ~ a helpless female! 'Despicable, sirrah ~ Dee~spicable!

YEAH!

THAT AIN'T NO FRAIL NOR HELPLESS FEMALE! THAT BAGNABBED OL' HARDSHELL LIZARD KNOCKED ME OVER-BOARD!

What? I cannot believe that this golden-eyed creat-ture would go demean herself~

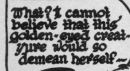

THEM GOL' SPECKLE EYES IS FROM MY MAM'S SIDE~ PERTY, AIN'T THEY?

FROM PA I GITS MY HIGH PITCH FALSETTIO VOICE WHEN I SING AN' GRAMPA INHERITED TO ME MY GREEN BALL-HEADED HEAD.

My word, sir! Your attire is strange!

ON ACCOUNT I IS DRESS UP TO DEE-LIVER A LOVE POEM~ WANNA HEAR IT?

HE SINGS IN A TREE-MOUNDOUS HIGH FALSETTIO. SO STAN' BACK!

IT'S THEM **ROOSIAN FELLERS**! THEY IS THRUN A **GUIDED MIZZLE**! *IT SCRUMMED PAST ME GOIN' NINE HUNNERD MILE A HOUR!* HEAD FOR HIGH GROUND, FRIENDS!

Land! You say a guided missile s'ped past you aloft?

YEP-- IT GUV OUT A VERY **HIGH PINCH** SCREAM AN' WHINE.

Why, that was your falsetto singing!

RIGHT---**SO** HIGH PITCH THAT IT GOES **CLEAR** OUTEN SIGHT!

NOSSIR! THIS WAS A **ROOSIAN FLYIN' SORCER**!

I assure you, friend, it was the voice of the turtle here~~~~

YOU GUYS GONNA TAKE A **LIGHT VIEW** OF THIS ENEMY THREAT? WHAT **ARE** YOU, **SUBVERSIBLE**?

I TELL YOU I SAW THE **PILOT**-- HAD A KINDA OF A **YELLOW PERIL LOOK** ABOUT HIM---AND A KNIFE IN HIS TEETH.

VERY VERY SIGNI-FICANT.

THE DUCK HERE CLAIM HE SAW A **ROCKET** FULL OF **ENEMIES** ALL ARMED AN' *SMIRKIN'!*

GOR BLIMEY!

A RUDDY GROUP FROM **OTTER SPACE** NO DOUBT, 'EY, ALF?

REGGIE, YOU'VE **HIT** IT, LAD.

I **SAY** THERE, MATE, 'OP TO IT AN' REPORT TO THE AUTHORITIES THAT AN ARMY OF BARB'ROUS FREE BOOTERS FROM MARS IS ABOUT TO TAKE OVER THE GOVERNMENT--THINK OF IT, OL' CHAP, A **MARTIAN PRESIDENT,** MARTIAN **SENATE**--ALL IN CHARGE OF US **HUMAN** TYPES.

ALL RIGHT! *LET 'EM!* IF THAT'S THEIR ATTITUDE! LET'S NOT EVEN *WARN* 'EM--IF THEY'S LOOKIN' FOR *TROUBLE,* THEY GONNA **GIT** IT.

OTTER SPACE, EH? HUFF HUFF!

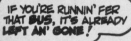

Chapter 12

DUMMIES ARE ENOUGH

"Old Lochinvar got me."

RIGHT CLEAR SLAMS OUTEN THE COUNTY-- AN' ALL A TIME HE TELLIN' ME HOW SAD AN' BROKE HEARTED HE IS 'CAUSE SHE WASN'T PAYIN' HIM NO MIND.

WULL, MEBBE HE TOOK OFF SO'S TO FIGGER WHICH FRACTURE IS THE WORSE-- THE BROKE HEART OF ISN'T GOT HER OR THE BROKE HEART OF IS.

GIT OFF!

THESE SILHOUETTES SURE SAVES A MESS OF DRAWIN'.

WHAT IN THE WIDE EVER LOVIN' BLUE EYED WORLD IS WE GONE TELL SIS BOOMBAH?

NOTHIN'.

THE HON. OL' WES

MAURER

NOTHIN'? HOW, UNDER SUCH CALAMITABOBBLE CIRCLESTANCES, KIN YOU SAY WE AIN'T GONE TELL HER NOTHIN'? HER BRIDEGROOM IS TOOK OFF FER MEXICO!

SHE'LL FIND THAT OUT SINGLEHANDED!

WHAT A LAGGERFOOTED FRAIDY-CAT ATTITUDE... AIN'T YOU GOT NO PUBLIC SPIRITED SPIRIT?

YEAH.

DON'T FORGET:

H____ GOT NO FURY LIKE A WOMAN SCORNED.

OL' WES

WHAT'S YOU MEAN ... H____?

NOT SO LOUD! NOT SO LOUD! YOU HEARD ME ... H____.

TROUBLE WITH YOU, POGO, IS YOU SPOILS THE FUN -- WHY SHOULDN'T WE TELL MIZ SIS BOOMBAH THAT HER LOCKINGVAR IS DONE GONE WEST?

RIGHT.

THE GIRL JOHN

IT WOULD BE A INNERESTIN' CHANCE TO STUDY HUMAN EMOTIONS AN' REACTIONS, WOULNENT IT?

RIGHT.

S'POSE SHE BUS' OUT WITH A EN-HUMAN TYPE REACTION AN' YOU LANDS UP WITH A CASE OF BROKE LIMBS AN' LACERATIONS OF THE SKULL BONE?

Y'SEE WHAT I MEAN? THAT BOY CON-TINUAL TAKE THE INNOCENT FUN, JOY AN' GLEE OUTEN EVER' BLESSED THING!

OH, I 'GRES.

JOHN McALLISTER

POGO GOT A **DO-GOODER** COMPLEX. HE ALLUS TELLIN' SOMEBODY HOW TO ACT--- HE OUGHT TO BE THANKFUL US IS AROUN', ELSE WHO'D HE HAVE TO **TELL OFF** NOW AN' THEN?

RIGHT.

IF **YOU'LL ES-SCUSE ME**, OWL, I GONNA EAT OUTSIDE--- SEEM LIKE I AIN'T **WELCOME** INSIDE HERE-- A LI'L THANKS ONCE AN' A WHILE WOULDN'T HURT NONE--

RIGHT.

WAIT-- YOU NEEDS SUGAR.

AIN'T NO USE FER ME TO WEAR THESE **DUDS** NO MORE--WHAT WILL WE TELL **MIZ BOOMBAH?**

WULL, JES' TELLIN' HER THAT DEACON IS RUN OFF 'STEAD OF FACIN' **WEDDIN' BELLS** IS NOT ONLY **RISKY**-- BUT **DULL**-- US OUGHT TO MAKE UP A **ROMANTICAL STORY.**

HOW 'BOUT IF US TELLS HER THAT DEACON IS BEEN CHOSE **MR. AMERICA** AN' IS GONE OFF TO MARRY **MISS AMERICA** AN' THEY GONNA LIVE HAPPY EVER AFTER IN THE **WHITE HOUSE?** THAT'S PERTY ROMANTICAL.

I DON'T **RIGHTLY** B'LEEVE IT'S THE KIND OF A STORY WOULD APPEAL TO MIZ SIS BOOMBAH'S **FINER INSTINCTS** WHICH KIN BE PERTY **DANGEROUS** WHEN A-ROUSED.

Chapter 13

CAN WE EGGPLANT?

Something borrowed and someone blew.

THESE SEE-GARS OF ALBERT'S IS STRONGER NOR SWAMP WATER COFFEE··

THINK I OUGHT TO BRING SIS A PRESENT?

A EXCELLENT SUGGESTION! TELL MIZ BOOMBAH THAT DEACON LEF' THESE BEHINE WHEN HE RUN OFF AN' HE SEND 'EM WITH HIS LOVE.

GREAT! JES'GREAT.

NOW YOU GOES OVER AN' TELL HER THAT DEACON GOT CALLED HOME TO FRANCE TO HEAD THE SUMMIT BEIN' AS HE DIRECT IN LINE TO BE THE LOST DAUPHIN.

DIN'T KNOW HE WAS FRENCH.

THAT'S EXACTLY WHY HE GONNA MAKE SUCH A GOOD LOST DAUPHIN, HE AIN'T 'ZACKLY FRENCH AN' HE AIN'T 'ZACKLY NOT FRENCH, HE JES' PLAIN LOST --- JES' GREAT FER BEIN' HEAD MAN.

INNER-NATURAL POLITICS STUMPS ME.

HAN' ME YO' BOO-KAY~ HOW 'BOUT IF I CRUNCHES DOWN INSIDE A CONTAINER LIKE MIZ RACKETY COON'S GARBAGE CAN AN' DISGUISES MYSELF LIKE A POTTED PLANT AN' BLOWS SWEET MUSIC···

MIZ R. COON TRASH

ON THE MOUTH HARP HERE TO SOOTHE MIZ BOOMBAH·· POOT-THOOT-

VERY NICE.

R. KOON CASH

71

Chapter *14*

CAN WE CORN?

In which we know
it all wreaks of vengeance.

NOW YOU STEP OUT AN' TELL HER THE DEACON'S *RUN OFF,* THEN GIVE HER A LIVERWURST SAMWICH WHILST I BLOW SAD MUSIC ON THE MOUTH HARP.

MIZ BOOMBAH···I HEARS THE DEACON'S IN LOVE OF YOU AN' I THUNK I BETTER SPEAK UP AN'···

POOT! POOT POOT POOT 🎵 POOT 🎵🎵

You too, Dear Boy?

I COME OVER TO TELL YOU SUMPIN··· DO YOU HEAR A SAD *MYSTERIOUS* MUSIC···?

POOT POOT

IT'S SAD, ALL RIGHT. WHAT'S YOUR MESSAGE, DOLL?

THE DEACON·· ··UH··GULB·· OOG··ULP·· ··THE DEACON·· GOOLP··DEA· ··OO··GOLM

POOT! POOT POOT

WHY, DOLL, YOU'RE *OVERCOME!*

I'LL PUT THIS BAG OVER CHURCHY'S HEAD-- IT'LL CURE HIS **HICCUPS** AN' THEN HE KIN TELL HIS MESSAGE.

OH, I'D GIVE A **PERTY** TO KNOW WHAT IT IS.

ACTUAL, HE'S A LI'L **SKEERT** TO TELL YOU ON ACCOUNT IT'S ABOUT THE **DEACON** IS *RUN OFF* AN' LEFT **YOU** WAITIN' AT THE CHURCH SO TO SPEAK; AS YOU'LL AGREE, A **TICKLISH SUBJECK.**

EEAARROWWFGH!

HIC!

IF THAT'S A TICKLISH SUBJECK, SHE **NIC** DON'T SEEM SO **NIC** TICKLED.

OH LUCKY ME DIN'T TELL ME! I COULD KILL ANYBODY'D TELL ME THAT!

LET'S TAKE THE HINT.

ONE THING BOTHERS ME, TURTLE. YOU STARTED OUT CARRYIN' A **BOX OF SEEGARS** TO GIVE SIS BOOMBAH.

BUT YOU WOUND UP CARRYIN' **LIVERWURST SAMWICHES** -- HOW COME?

WULL--

Chapter 15

CAN WE SUCCOTASH?

How long is a memory?

80

Chapter *16*

STRING WE STRONGBEANS

Not every judge has the courage
of his convictions.

LOVED ONES IS SUFFER'N' AN' YOU, YOU CRAVEN KNAVE, YOU CARES NOT A WHIT!

YOU IS A KNAVEN-CRAVE YO'SELF.. NO LOVED ONES IS SUFFER'N'.

OL' BILL COYLE

WHAT ABOUT THE DEACON? WHO KNOWS WHAT DANGERS HE FACES..? LOST IN THE WOODS....

SNUCKS! HE AIN'T IN NO DANGER AN' I AIN'T IN LOVE OF HIM.

HULL, MIZ GIS BOOMBAH IS IN LOVE OF HIM ... SO THERE!

SO, SHE IS GONE AFTER HIM COZ HE LEAVE HER LOOKIN' FOR HIM AT THE CHURCH DOOR.

THAT'S WHAT I MEAN! HE FACES A UNKNOWED AN' UNEXPLORED PERIL WHEREIN THE FOOT OF MAN IS NEVER TROD!

NOW, WHAT I PREE-POSE FOR YOU TO DO IS GO FIND OL' DEACON AN' RESCUE HIM OUTEN HIS PREDICKLE-MINTS.

I IS BUSY.

VON WETTERS (DE BOAT)

THE GENERAL

ANYBODY KIN BE BUSY ... BUT WHO, WHO, PRAY TELL, WHO GITS A CHANCE TO BE A HERO EVERY DAY?

A GOOD QUESTION, ... WHO? WHO INDEED?

Chapter *17*

FOR THE MORN

The Pathfinders' Founder.

HA! NOTHING TO **THAT** PROBLEM-- **WE'LL JUST RUB STICKS TOGETHER** FOR **FIRE!**

AN' FOR FOOD?

FOR FOOD--WE'LL CATCH THINGS WITH OUR **BARE HANDS!**

HURRY BACK, NOW, Y'HEAR?

US'LL SEE YOU SOON'S WE BRINGS THE DEACON **BACK ALIVE.**

MORE OR LESS.

MIZ BOOMBAH AIN'T FEARED OF **MAN** NOR **BEAST** NOR **NOTHIN'.**

NOTHIN' 'CEPT MICE.

MICE? YOU MEAN **US?**

HECK, NO! **US** AIN'T MICE... WE'RE LI'L' **BATS!**

SURE! WE **FLIES,** SEE?

WOOP! IS YOU **SURE** WE AIN'T **MICE?**

NAW! HE CAN FLY GOOD ENOUGH, EXCEPT HE KEEP TRYIN' TO HOLD ONTO HIS **HAT.**

OH, FELLOWS.

THING I LIKE ABOUT THIS **CAMPIN' TRIP** IS WE GOT SOME-BODY TO BE **FOURTH WHEEL** ON THE CARD GAME...

YOU MEAN THE GIRL WHAT'S 'FRAID OF **MICE**?

YEP-- UH, YOU GOT A **QUEEN** OR TWO THERE--? I GOT THE LOVELIEST PAIR OF KINGS.

NOPE.. JES' JACKS -- NINE OF 'EM.

A GIRL LIKE **MIZ BOOMBAH** WOULD MAKE A GOOD CUSTOMER IN CASE YOU EVER BUILD A **BETTER MOUSE TRAP.**

WHAT GOOD IS A **BETTER MOUSE TRAP**?-- 'TAIN'T THE **BETTER MICE** SHE'S FEARED OF, IT'S THAT **ROUGH ELEMENT**, THE **WORSER MICE**...

IF YOU RASCALS WERE **GENTLEMEN** YOU'D TALK OF SOMETHIN' BESIDES **MONSTERS!**

PLEASE DON'T MAKE SO MUCH **NOISE** CRACKIN' WOOD, MA'M-- IT'S **HARD** TO CONCENTRATE.

CRACK

I'VE A FEELING THAT **NONE** OF YOU LITTLE **TRAIL MONGERS** KNOWS WHERE YOU'RE GOING.

HE SURE DON'T, MA'M'. IF HE HAD A HORSE WHAT **WOULD** DRINK HE COULDN'T LEAD HIM TO **WET** GROUND.

A FINE WAY TO TALK ABOUT OUR CHUM.

WHO?

YOU! OUR LEADER, PRO-TEM, THE FEARLESS.

I AIN'T LEADIN'. **YOU** IS.

ME?!
I AIN'T LED NOTHIN' SINCE I SPEAR HEADED THE VOLUNTEERS INTO THE LADIES' SMOKIN' ROOM DURIN' THE GREAT FORT MUDGE FIRE AN' PICNIC OF 19-OUGHT-23. IT MUS' BE *HIM*.

WHOOIE! MY *LAND!* THIS IS A *FOOT-WEARYIN'* COUNTRY.

I GOT A COMPASS HERE ... WILLED US BY OUR WANDER'N' UNCLE, *DIMBO JEFFERSON.*

HMMPH.. NO *WONDER* HE WANDERED. THER' AIN'T NO *DIRECTION* ON IT BUT *SOUTH*. FOUR SOUTHS!

WHAT ELSE *IS* THERE?

IT SEEMS *IMPOSSIBLE* THAT YOU BOY BIRD WATCHERS COULD BE SO *IGNORANT* OF WOODSY LORE.

OUR MOTTO IS "ULTIMA RATIO REGUM." OR "NOTHIN' IS IMPOSSIBLE."

NOW, SUPPOSE YOU WANT TO KNOW WHICH WAY THE WIND IS BLOWING, FIRST YOU WET A FINGER LIKE *SO* ...

ANY OL' BODY'S FINGER, I GUESS?

THEN, *HOLDING* IT ALOFT, WE DETECT THE DIRECTION OF THE-- *WOK!*

THE WOK? A DRY ARABIAN RIVER.

YOU SHOULDNTNA SQUEEZED ME!

YEAH! PERSONAL, HE'S JES' AS INNOCENT AS A NEW-BORE CHILE.

90

Chapter *18*

MASTERFUL MUSTACHE

Friends of our childhood
and other haunts of the past.

We wondered what had become of you, Sir; thought you were finished ~~~ All the time you've been back here working, eh, Sir?

YEP·· I DECIDED TO TURN OVER A NEW LEAF·· I'M DOIN' SOMETHIN' CONSTRUCTIVE FOR FOLKS.

That's nice of you, Sir~

PLEASE LET ME FINISH ·· ALTHO I AGREE WITH YOUR INTERRUPTION·· I'M IN THE *DOOR* BUSINESS ·· THE SWAMP *ALWAYS* NEEDED DOORS.

Doors for houses, That right Sir?

RIGHT, AN' I'LL GUARANTEE EVERY ONE OF 'EM··· I'LL STAND BEHIND *EVERY DOOR.*

TROUBLE WITH *YOU,* DEAC, IS YOU BEEN OVERWORKIN' YOURSELF···· YOU GOT A *HAGGERT* LOOK ON YOU FIT TO *CHOKE* A *HE-HAWG*····· WAIT'LL YOU TASTES OL' CHARLIE'S *FRY,* HERE····

THIS···· AN' THE FRESH TYPE OF AIR WILL MAKE A *NEW MAN* OF YOU····· YOU PROBLY GOT A *APPETITE* WORKED UP····

Yes'

PLEASE, LET ME FINISH, DEAC, I'D LIKE TO SAY ONE WORD ABOUT THE *FINE* YOUNG MAN WHO GIVE SO MUCH OF HIS TIME TO PREPARE THESE FISH···

Yum

LET ME FINISH···BEAR WITH ME·· A WORD, IF I MAY···THEM FISH BEEN PREPARED BY THE *FINEST FRYER*···THE MOST *BRILLIANT* YOUNG MAN WITH A PAN THAT I EVER SEEN···*DEE-LISH, HUH, KID?*

Itt

YEP, DEAC · I FIGGER WHAT THIS SWAMP NEEDS IS *DOORS*···LIKE I SAID, I'LL MAKE 'EM AN' I'LL *GUARANTEE* 'EM···FOLKS'LL KNOW I *STAND BEHIND EVERY SINGLE ONE!*

They sure will ··

CRACK!

PLEASE·· *DON'T INTERRUPT, DEAC*···LET ME *FINISH*·· LET ME FINISH···NOW AS I WAS SAYIN'···UH-

MY GOODNESS, DEACON, WHO WERE YOU OUT HERE *WITH*?

Wull~~

LOOK!

YEOW!

SCUSE US

Evidently they didn't want to startle you by showing who they was'~~

I'M AFEARED US WILL HAFTA KEEP THESE BAGS OVER OUR HEADS, OTHERWISE THAT CHICKEN FROM **PROVIDENCE** MIGHT **RECOGNIZE** US.

SHE BIG ENEMY, HUH?

NO WORRY, CHIEF.. ME, **CHARLIE**, ALWAYS STAND BY **YOU**.

Chapter 19

DEATHLY DUMPLINGS

In which we discover
that some things
are always over some people's heads.

NOW GRUNDOON IS READY TO MAKE HIS *FIRST* PUBLIC RECITATION USIN' ALL TWO OF HIS NEW WORDS ---GO AHEAD, SON.

PSQRLD.

BYE BYE PTX SQBZ VNTNN STPMQR RR KLMNPQRS.

CMQTZ LKVN PDM TPSLKX! BYE.

HAH! AN AGITATOR! AN' SPEAKING A FOREIGN TONGUE...I MUST TAKE NOTES.

DRAT! NO PENCIL --- BUT I CAN REMEMBER IT -- SOUNDS LIKE *BAFFIN* OR PERHAPS *PATAGONIAN* -- "*ZGBLKVMPDMS!*" THAT HAS A VICIOUS SOUND TO IT.

MPSGRVLD! ZGLBKR! THAT'S WHAT THAT FOREIGN *AGITATOR* WAS SAYING -- I MUST REPEAT IT 'TIL I CAN GET HOME AN' MAKE NOTES --

GOSH-- THERE'S OL' MOLE.

MUSTN'T FERGIT IT -- *MPSGRVLD! ZGLBKR!*

MPSGRVLD ZGLBKR

HEY, MOLE! WHAT'S THE GOOD WORD?

MPSGRVLD! ZGLBKR! MPSGRVLD! ZGLBKR! MPSGRVLD! ZGLBKR!

?

THESE DAGNAB BAGS OVER OUR HEADS MAKES IT HARD TO HEAR--- I COULD OF SWORE HE SAID: "MPSGRVLD! ZGLBKR!" BUT WHY WOULD HE BE TALKIN' MESOPOTAMIAN?

THIS BAIT BAG SO LOUD INSIDE, CHARLIE CAN'T HEAR HIMS OWN SELF.

MPSGRVLD ZGLBKR MPSGRVLD ZGLBKR MPSGRVLD

CAN'T WAIT TO GIT HOME--- I'LL USE POGO'S HOUSE TO JOT DOWN THE MESSAGE I OVERHEARD THAT FOREIGN AGITATOR GIVE ---HMM-- MPSGRVLD ZGLBKR!

IT'LL KEEP WELL ENOUGH ON THE BACK OF POGO'S GROCERY LIST --MPSGRVLD ZGLBKR! HAH! SUCH A SINGULARLY SINISTER SOUND!

HERE HE COMES OUT OF POGO'S PLACE.

WHAT CAN IT MEAN? A SECRET FORMULA --FOR A BOMB PERCHANCE? "MPSGRVLD ZGLBKR!"

HEY, H'LO THERE, MOLE-- DON'T YOU KNOW YOUR OL' FRIEND?

SO THAT'S THE WAY IT IS! IGNORED AN' SPURNT BY OL' FRIENDS -- THEY DON'T KNOW ME NO MORE! CHARLIE, THERE AIN'T NOTHIN' I'M SAYIN' FOR THE RECORD, AS FICKLE, MIND YOU, AS FICKLE FATE.

I DON'T GIVE A *WILLYBONE* IF THAT *CHICKEN FROM PROVIDENCE* *DOES* SEE ME--I'M TAKIN' OFF THIS *DADBLANG FISH BAG!*

IT'S STUCK!

DING IT! IT *IS* SORTA GROWED ON ME--- THEM OL' FISH IS KINDA MOGGLED UP THE INSIDE--*OOMPH!*

MINE TOO-- HOW WHY ARE YOU SCARED OF THIS *BOOMBO*?

UH-HUH-HUH--*ME SCARED, CHARLIE?* CHARLIE, *LET ME SET THE RECORD STRAIGHT RIGHT NOW*-- MIZ BOOMBAH WAS MY OLD *MANUAL TRAININ' TEACHER* UP IN MY *ALMA MATER*---I DON'T WANNA *UPSET* HER BY SHOWIN' UP ALL OF A SUDDEN...

NOT SCARED THOUGH, HUH, CHIEF?

NO--BUT *SHE'S SENSITIVE*-- SHE WAS WORKIN' INSIDE A BOX IN 19-OUGHT-26 AN' I STARTED, UNKNOWN TO HER, TO PRACTICE A MAGIC TRICK CALLED "SAWIN' A WOMAN IN HALF." WELL--IT TOUCHED HER, *DEEPLY,* AN' TO THIS DAY I-UH-HUH HUH-HUH-

FIGGER WE'LL ALWAYS BE IN THE BAG THIS WAY, CHIEF?

NO... THESE THINGS WEAR OFF-- FOLKS'LL FORGET.

In this our Heroes learn
that it is very dangerous
to be alive in these days.

HAH! SUCH COMPLACENCY WHILE DOOM PILES UP ON OUR DOORSTEP.

I AIN'T NEITHER COMPLACENT!

DON'T WASTE TIME ARGUIN'-- LOOK AT THIS!

BUT HE KEEP CALLIN' ME COMPLACENT--- WHILE ALL THE TIME I IS DOIN' MY DUTY AS A CITIZEN--- NIGHT AN' DAY!

MY!

LYIN' AWAKE WORRYIN' AT NIGHT -- AFEARED TO SLEEP IN CASE I GITS BLOWED UP IN MY BED AN' NEVER KNOWS!

BOY! BOY! BOY! BOY!

AN' ALL DAY--SCANNIN' THE SKY-- NOT KNOWIN' WHEN ---WONDERIN' WHETHER TO WEAR PAJAMAS THAT NIGHT SO'S TO BE FOUND DECENT-- WONDERIN' WHETHER TO TAKE A BATH---WHETHER TO PACK A LIGHT LUNCH--

HOO BOY!

I DON'T LIKE THESE MODERN DAY DISASTERS WHAT CONSISTS OF TEN YEARS OF WORRY AN' TEN SECONDS OF BOOM AN' WANGO!

THIS IS SOME FORMULA.

IN THE OL' DAYS OF FREE ENNERPRIZES FOLKS COULD SIT 'ROUND HAPPY AS CLAMS 'TIL ALL OF A SUDDEN SOME BOY'D RUSH IN AN' HOLLER..

MM-UMP! LOOKY THERE!

WHOOHEE! THE JUTE MILL IS EXPLODED!

THEN FOLKS'D RUSH AROUN' AN' SOONER OR LATER SOMEBODY'D GIT **HURT** OUT OF *THAT* AN' YOU'D GIT **HOT COFFEE** AN' **DONUTS**---AN'--BUT YOU DIN'T HAFTA SIT AROUN' WORRYIN' 'BOUT IT FOR **SIX MONTHS** 'HEAD OF TIME.

THE JUTE MILL IS EXPLODED! CHURCHY HOLLERED IT OUT!

HORRORS!

WHICH WAY IS IT?

WHICH WAY IS *WHAT*?

THE *JUTE MILL!* ARE WE RUNNIN' TO IT OR FROM IT?

JUTE MILL?

YOU *KNOW* WE AIN'T GOT NO JUTE MILL.

HE WAS A SETTIN' NEXT TO ME AN' ALL OVER SUDDEN HE CALL OUT "THE JUTE MILL IS EXPLODED" BUT WE DON'T GOT NO JUTE MILL...

AN' YOU GOT SO EXCITED YOU RUN OFF ANYWAYS, HUH?

THEN, TOO, IN THE OLD DAYS THE WARNIN'S OF THE DISASTERS HAD A BETTER SOUND ON 'EM.

NOWADAYS IF ANYTHIN'S GONNA *LAY YOU WASTE* YOU GITS FIRST TO HEAR A *SIGH-REEN--* A NASTY NOISE WORSE'N ACTUAL *INJURY* OR *DEATH*

WHEEEEEEEEEE

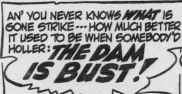

AN' YOU NEVER KNOWS *WHAT* IS GONE STRIKE--- HOW MUCH BETTER IT USED TO BE WHEN SOMEBODY'D HOLLER: *THE DAM IS BUST!*

LEAST YOU KNOWED WHAT YOU'S GONE *DIE* OF.

THAT BOY'S GOT A *PENCHANT* FOR *VISIONS!* HAS THE SWAMP GOT A DAM?

YES! AN' IT BETTER OF *REALLY BUST* OR I'SE COMIN' BACK PERSONAL AN' QUENCH THAT PENCHANT!

?

ME AN' MISS BOOMBAH *RUN* AN' *RUN* AN' *ROUSED* UP EVER'BODY IN THE SWAMP AN' THE *DAM NEVER BUST AT ALL.*

WHY *SHOULD* IT?

YOU SCROOCHED OUT THAT IT DID! YOU'RE A DOGBONE *ALARMIST* AN' *PORTENTATE* OF *DOOMS!*

I WAS ONLY THINKIN' QUIETLY TO *MYSELF.*

THAT WAS SOME OF THE *LOUDEST OUTDOOR TYPE THINKIN'* WHAT EVER RANG A DECIBEL AN' *UNTRUE* BESIDES.

HOW'S YOU *KNOW* IT WAS UNTRUE? ·· DID YOU RUN OVER TO THE DAM?

'*COURSE NOT*, US REFUGEED OUR WAY TO *POGO'S* HOUSE AN' HE FED US COOKIES AN' MILK AN' 'SPLAINED THAT THE DAM *CAUGHT FIRE* IN 1932 AN' THE GUMMINT AIN'T REPLACED IT.

IF I'D KNOWED THAT I'D OF FLED THE DISASTER MYSELF.

LET'S GIT ON OVER TO YO' PLACE AN' COOK UP A *BAIT OF GREENS* AN' TALK OVER THIS HERE *FORMULA.*

I RESENTS YOU THINKIN' I WAS *SHOUTIN'* BEFORE. WHEN *I* SINGS OR SHOUTS, IT'S *HIGH PINCH-LIKE.*

LIKE *THIS.*

OUT OF EAR AN' EYE SHOT.

WHAT'D YOU HOLLER THAT TIME?

A BRAN' NEW MESSAGE, TO WIT: THE *CHEROKEES* IS *EXCAPED* FROM FORT MUDGE.

TO THE STOCKADE, MEN! BRING IN THE CATTLE AN' WOMENFOLKS ··· DON'T LET 'EM TAKE YOU ALIVE!

PUT US DOWN, HOUN' DOG --- I JES' WAS SHOWIN' OWL HOW **HIGH** I CAN SCREECH --- I MERE HOLLERED "**THE CHEROKEES IS COMIN'**," AS A TEST.

MY SAKES! I GOT A **HIGH PINCH BAR** LIKE MOG' DOGS DO --- LET'S HEAR YOU HOLLER SOMETHIN' ELSE.

THIS TIME I'LL JES' HOLLER "HEY, SAM!"

BOY! BOY!

THEY DID IT AGAIN! A INNERPLANERARY 'SHIP MWOOSH BY ME ALL LOADED WITH SMIRKIN' ENEMIES AN' HORSE-PISTOLS!

WHAT *NONSENSE!* AN' *US* WITH SERIOUS WORK TO DO.

Chapter *21*

GRACE OUR FESTIVE BOARD

Awe struck out
on three high-pitched bawls.

111

Chapter 22

FREE FROMENTY

Cave canem!
Spelunk! Spelunk!

I'VE A HUNCH THAT THE MYSTERIOUS STRANGER *IS* HIDING IN THIS CAVE... ---HAND ME A TORCH---

I LEFT MY TORCH IN MY SUNDAY PANTS... *WE TOLE YOU AN' TOLE YOU:* THAT'S THE *BAIT BUCKET* YOU'M STUCK INTO.

AT LEAST GIVE ME A HAND SO I CAN *CLIMB IN* AFTER HIM----

AARGH! HE'S A SLIPP'RY ONE----SEE, HE'S TRIPPED ME! *DO GET A LIGHT!* LEND A HAND BEFORE THIS *QUACKSALVER* SLIPS BY THE DRAGNET!

HE JUMPED INTO A HOLE! *LIKE AS NOT HE'S PLOTTING A NEW MOVE*----BRING A LIGHT INTO THIS CAVERN---*THE STALACTITES ARE BEAUTIFUL!*

HE GOT THE VERTYGOO...

FROM TIME TO TIME I'LL ISSUE BULLETINS ON MY PROGRESS IN CHASING THE MYSTERIOUS STRANGER IN THIS CAVE.

NO MATTER WHAT YOU CALLS IT, IT'S STILL A *BAIT BUCKET!*

THIS IS GONE *FAR ENOUGH!* WE GONE GIT YOU UP AN' OUT OF *THERE.*

114

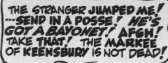

THE STRANGER JUMPED ME! ...SEND IN A POSSE! HE'S GOT A BAYONET! AFGH! TAKE THAT! THE MARKEE OF KEENSBURY IS NOT DEAD!

HALLOO! HALLOO! CAN YOU HEAR ME? I'M STUCK IN THE CAVERN... THE MYSTERIOUS STRANGER FLUNG ME INTO A UNDERGROUND LAGOON!

GOT A CAN-OPENER ON YOU?

I'M CRAWLING DEEPER INTO THIS CAVERN NOW; STILL AFTER THE MYSTERIOUS STRANGER!

C'MON, WE'LL PULL THE BAIT BUCKET OFF MOLE'S HEAD.

WE GOTTA CONVINCE HIM HE AIN'T IN NO CAVE---

HALLOO! I'M HOT ON HIS TRAIL... HALLOO!

HALLOO! HO, OUT THERE! CAN YOU HEAR ME?

WOOH! WE PULLED OFF THE BUCKET BOTTOM.

OOMP!

VIEW HALLOO! I'VE COME TO DAYLIGHT--- CRAWLED ALL THE WAY THRU---HA! A NASTY FACE IS PEERING AT ME--- IT'S THE VILLAIN I'M AFTER!

115

...*YOWTCH!*

CAREFUL OUT THERE! THERE'S TWO OF 'EM HERE IN THE CAVE. ONE HAS A CRUEL FACE AN' THE OTHER IS ARMED WITH A SET OF KNITTING NEEDLES ···*HALLOO CAN YOU HEAR ME?*

SO YOU IS FIGGERED A WAY TO GIT MOLE OUTEN THE BUCKET?

YEP, OL' RACKETY·COON CHILE IS GONE HOME TO BORRY THE LOAN OF SOME LARD OR BUTTER TO SLIPPERY UP MOLE'S HEAD.

THEN WE PULLS HIM OUT SLICK AS A WEASEL.

ALL SET UNCLE POGO!

. HOT DOG! HE'S A-SLUMMIN' OUT!

HERE HE COME!

DOGBONE! HE GOT *HURT!* GIT A DOCTOR! THE BOY IS ALL *GORE AN' MASSACREE!*

AW, NO, UNCLE POGO, I COULDN'T FIND NO *BUTTER* SO I BRUNG OVER SOME *RAS'BERRY JAM!*

117

Chapter *23*

FLEES THE FLOOD

Hark! Hark!
The trees do bark.

120

121

MY **KEEN** BRAIN IS WHOPPIN' OUT IDEAS ON HOW US KIN DISGUISE OURSELFS AS **NATURAL-BORN SCENERY** AN' THEN **LEAP** OUT ON THE MYSTERIOUS STRANGER.

PHOO

YOU, FER EXAMPLE, KIN HIDE UNDER BENEATH OF THE WATER AN' MAKE OUT YOU IS A **TURTLE**.

I IS A... TURTLE... A DRY TYPE LAND TURTLE.

THAT FISH LOOK ABOUT DONE--AN' **YOU** OWL, YOU COULD LAY AROUND ON A PILE OF JUNK AN' PRETEND LIKE YOU IS A **DEAD CHICKEN** IN A **PUBLIC DUMP**.

LIKE FITZES AN' HITZES?

AN' IF **YOU** KEEPS EATIN' ALL THE FISH, YOU KIN PASS FER A **DEAD ALLIGATOR**, PERVIDIN' I KEEPS MY STRENGTH.

AN' IF ALBERT PLAYS HIS CARDS RIGHT.

THERE'S ONLY **ONE WAY** TO **FOOL** THE MYSTERIOUS STRANGER, US IS **GOTTA** DISGUISE OURSELFS AS NATURAL **FAUNIA** AN' **FLORIA** .... YOU, OWL, GITS TO BE A **DEAD CHICKEN** ON A PUBLIC DUMP!

I WON'T DO IT-- WE AIN'T GOT NO **PUBLIC DUMP** -

IF IT COULD BE A **PRIVATE** DUMP, HERE'S MY **PERSONAL** COLLECTION.

NOW THAT I IS GOT YOU TWO DISGUISED GOOD, (OWL BEIN'A DEAD CHICKEN AN' CHURCHY BEIN'A BABBLIN' BROOK), I GOTTA DIG UP A DISGUISE FOR ME.

HMM... MEBBE I COULD USE THIS.

YOU KIN IF YOU GIVES ME CREDIT, SAYIN' IT'S FROM THE PRIVATE JUNK PILE OF CHURCHY LA FEMME.

HOW 'BOUT IF I PUTS IT ON MY HEAD AN' PRETENDS I IS A TREE WITH A BIRD HOUSE ON IT?

TRY IT FER SIZE ANYWAYS.

GEE, KIN YOU MAKE A NOISE LIKE A BIRD HOUSE?

CAW! CAW! PEEP! PEEP!

IT GIVE HIM THAT NEW FLAT LOOK.

NOT ALL OF US OUGHT TO BE ON DUTY ALL THE TIME-- WHY NOT SPELL EACH OTHER?

WHY NOT?

EACH OTHER-- E-E-CHES-O-U-T-H-R-

YOU GO ON DUTY FIRST, BEIN'A TREE AN' BIRDHOUSE---HE'LL REST AN' PLOT OUT WHAT TO DO NEXT...

RIGHT.

EVERY BOY GOTTA LEARN WHAT THE TREES IS·· THAT'N IS IRON·WOOD, BETTER KNOWED AS BUTTON·BALL OR COTTON·FOOT.

THAT HOMELY ONE THERE WITH THE BIRD HOUSE ON IT IS BITTER·BARK OR UGLY ELMLY.

IT LOOK PERTY LUMPY.

WITH MY TRUSTY KNIFE I KIN STEAL OFF ALONE AWAY FROM ALL SNEAKS·········

··INTO THE DEEPNESS OF THE WOODS WHERE NOBODY KIN WATCH ME AN' UN·DISTURBED I KIN CARVE ONTO A VIRGIN TRUNK THE NAME WITH HEART ENTWINED OF HER WHOM I A·DORE··

I WOULDN'T DO THAT IF I WAS YOU, FRIEND.

SO··YOU AIN'T A REAL TREE.

THAT SNEAK!

126

Chapter 24

FRAUGHTFUL FRUGAL'S FLOORED

Wherein we see
that not everyone can live in a birdhouse
and keep his feet on the ground.

130

I QUITS! I BEEN WAITIN' TO TRAP A MYSTERIOUS STRANGER AN' NONE COME ALONG!

WAITIN' THERE I WAS, SUSPECTIN' AN' THINKIN'--QUIET AN' READY, --READY TO SPRING THE TRAP-- AN' NO MYSTERIOUS SUSPECTS COME ALONG--IT'S UNFAIR!

OL' DEACON AN' HOUN' DOG AN' BUN RABBIT, TOO, IS GITTIN' A RAW DEAL--RUNNIN' THEY IS, TO THE RESCUE-- CAN'T REMEMBER WHERE OR WHO-- HOW'S THAT FOR UNFAIR?

OH, IT BEEN LIKE THAT THE WHOLE BLESSED YEAR. ALL OUR RESCUIN' AN' RUNNIN' AN' WORRYIN' AN' CREEPIN-UP-ON-THE-ENEMY AN' NOTHIN' TO SHOW FOR IT--- THEY AIN'T NO JUSTICE.

PUFF-PUFF-PUFF-PUFF-PUFF

WHERE'S Y'ALL RUNNIN' TO?

TO THE --- PUFF...RESCUE

SOME DING DONG DOLT IS GOT HIS--PUFF--PUFF---SELF TRAPPED INTO A--PUFF--BIRDHOUSE.

WHO IS THIS NUMPSKULL?

OL' ALBERT.

SOME BIRD BRAIN IS ALLUS CAUSIN' OTHER FOLKS TROUBLE.

YEP... AN' I CARRY THE HOSE.

DON'T YOU THINK YOU OUGHT TO CHASE AFTER DEACON AN' HOUN' DOG AN' BUN RABBIT 'FORE THEY WEARS OUT THEM-SELFS?

YOU'RE RIGHT! IF ANY-BODY GONE BE A HERO-TO-THE-RESCUE I IS THE MAN FER THE JOB.

NO! NO! THEY IS OUT TO RESCUE YOU.

THEY GONE RESCUE ME? WHAT'S-A-MATTER WITH ME?

WULL--THAT'S A TOUGH QUESTION, BUT THEY THINKS YO' IS STILL TRAPPED IN A BIRD-HOUSE--THEY GONE SAVE YOU.

IN THAT CASE, LEAVE 'EM BE--THEY IS ENGAGED IN A NOBLE WORK--LET US NOT DISTURB 'EM IN THEIR FINEST HOUR--IF A MAN IS FIXED TO SAVE YO' LIFE IT WON'T PAY TO INNER-FERE.

MEBBE A BIRD HOUSE IS WHERE YOU FITS BEST.

YOU, SIRRAH, ARE *NOTHIN' BUT A RABBIT!*

HAH! STEP OUTSIDE AN' SAY THAT!

I ALREADY SAID IT OUTSIDE..

YOU DID *IN-DEED.*

AN' BESIDES YOU *IS* A RABBIT.

NOT A "NOTHIN'-BUT-A-RABBIT" THO'--

So! I've been bilked! *Bee-trayed* and bamboozled ~~~ Albert never *was* in trouble. *Yet* I ran my legs off to *save* him ~~~

Ha! Such ignominomminy. *I'm through* with the *vapid* vacillations of these vacant villains ~~~ I shall *never* join them again in any *sort* of enter-prise ~~~

WE'S ALL GONE EAT TOGETHER, DEAC---- *COME-A-RUNNIN'!*

~~~*enterprise* as long as *I* live! ~~~ *beginning next year!*

134

Chapter 25

HEAR YE! HEAR YE!

How to build a dirigible
in your own hat
without a paddle.

HOW **OUT**-RAGEOUS! *SCANDULUM MAGNATUM!* A BASE PERFIDY! A REPREHENSIBLE ODIUM! AN' ODOROUS MALEVOLENCE! A SHABBY INFAMY! THEY SULLY A **BLOT** UPON OUR OBLOQUY!

BY NAB, THEM WORMS WAS SNAKES IN THE GRASS...I BEEN *MAD!* ...*THEY AIN'T NO OIL HERE*...ALL I SAID 'BOUT THEM OTHER FLIM FLAMS *NOW* GOES FOR THE WORMS, TOO.

GOOD NEWS! *GREAT GOOD NEWS!* OH, TERRIFIC TIDINGS!

HE'S *DEAD!*

BRAH-HA-HO HOO BOO WAW WUFFA!

WHAT'S EATIN' ON YOU?

IF YOU IS DEAD --IT SPOILS MY GOOD NEWS...A WHOLE SUNNY DAY IS SHOT.

137

IS YOU ALIVE ENOUGH TO HEAR OF MY *BRAN' NEW PLAN* FOR BEIN' *MILLIONAIRES* AN' STUFF LIKE THAT?

MAN, IS YOU *CRAZY?* DON'T I LOOK ALIVE?

ONE QUESTION AT A TIME --- NOW JES' LISTEN AT MY SCHEME --- *WE GITS TO MAKE NEW YEAR'S RESOLUTIONS FOR OTHER FOLKS* ---

WE'VE *DID* THAT.

NOT LIKE THIS! WE *ALSO* BREAKS THE RESOLUTION --- THEREBY SPARIN' OUR CLIENTS THE *INSUFFERABOBBLE PANGS OF* CONSCIENCE WHICH COMES FROM BREAKIN' THEIR WORD TO THEYSELFS.

WHY IS YOU GOT THAT BOOK?

IT'S A BOOK ON "*HOW TO BUILD A DIRIGIBLE*" WHICH I IS READIN' WHILST TALKIN' TO YOU IN CASE YOU *STUPIDLY* DON'T UNNERSTAN' ME AN' I WON'T BE WASTIN' MY TIME *COM-PLETE.*

HOW WOULD THIS NEW *RESOLUTIN'* BUSINESS OF YOURS WORK?

STEP INTO *POGO'S HOUSE* WITH ME JES' A SECOND.

HEIGHDY, POGO --- SCUSE US JES' A MINUTE --- *BEE-HOLE,* OWL, THERE IS A BATCH OF NEW BATCHED DOUGHNUTS --- *I* MAKES A RESOLUTION FOR YOU THAT YOU AIN'T GONE EAT *NO MORE DOUGHNUTS.*

YUM

BUT, *KNOWIN'* YO' *WEAK-WILLED WAYS*, I *QUICK* BREAKS THE *RESOL*-LUB-GLUB-*TION* AB GLOBBLE-*UGH*-GLUM *FOR YOU* -- GOOM

WHYN'T YOU WAIT 'TIL I'D *COOKED* EM?

YOU REALIZE, OF COURSE, POGO, THAT YOU GOT A *SICK* MAN ON YO' HANDS, AIN'T YOU?

A *SICK* MAN? ON *MY* HANDS? TURTLE GOT SICK OF *HIS OWN FREE-HAND* AN' WILL AN' SKILL.

HE SICKENED FROM EATIN' *YO' HOME MADE DOUGHNUTS* ---

OOG

HEAR HIM GROAN?

NOBODY INVITED *HIM* TO *EAT 'EM* -- THEY WASN'T EVEN COOKED AN' BESIDES "OOG" AIN'T *RIGHTLY* A GROAN ---

"OOG" *AIN'T* A GROAN? HOW *KIN* YOU SCOFF IN THE FACE OF SCIENTIFIC FACT? *(HAVE SOME BANANA PIE, TURTLE, IT'LL PERK YOU)* WHAT IS "OOG" IF IT AIN'T A GROAN?

...

TECH-KNUCKLE SPEAKIN' IT'D BE MORE OF A SOFT HICCUP.

YOU NOTICE MY PATIENT IS STILL *GROANIN'* FROM THE EE·FECTS OF YO' HOME MADE DOUGHNUTS.

OOG OOG

"OOG" AIN'T NO GROAN···IT'S A **SOFT HICCUP**···WHY IS YOU TOOK TO BED?

DOES YOU THINK A **HIPPOCRATICAL OATH** MEANS *NOTHIN'*?! US **HEALER**-TYPES GOT TO BE NEAR OUR LOVED ONES.

DO YOU FOR A MINUTE **SOO**-POSE THAT **THIS NOBLE YOUTH** WOULD BE LEFT ALONE ON HIS BED OF PAIN? **NO!** **I AIN'T PROUD!** I IS **LOYAL!** IF HE'S SICK···I IS SICK! OOG!

OOG

I DIN'T KNOW YOU WAS A **BONA FIDE** HIPPO-CRITICAL OAF.

BUT LONG AS YOU IS **BOTH** AT DEATH'S DOOR I DON'T FIGGER I OUGHT TO WASTE NONE OF THIS **BRUNSWICK STEW** ON NO **CORPSES.**

HERE'S MY FRIEND, **TURTLE,** AN' ME, **OWL,** ALL BACK SAFE AN' SOUND *AND* A-**HUNGERED**···STRAIGHT FROM A ENGAGEMINTS WITH *DEATH'S DOOR.*

YOU TWO WAS **TOO SICK TO WALK** UNTIL YOU GOT A NOSEFUL OF MY **BRUNSWICK STEW**···YOU CLAIMED YOU WAS *HALF-DEAD*···

AN' I IS···IIS·IS·IS!

NOTICE HOW **BRIGHT AN' BEAMIN'** IS MY **RIGHT-HANDED EYEBALL** -- WHERE-AS MY **LEF'-HAND EYEBALL** IS SLUGFUL AN' **GORMY** -- **NOW NOW** KIN WE CLEAR UP THIS **HALF-DEAD LOOK,** SIR?

QUICK US APPLIES A LI'L' OF DR. POGO'S **BRUNSWICK REMEDY** --- IN A FLASH WE SEES **BOTH** EYES SPARKLE WITH THE BEAUTY OF -- **HEY!**

NOW YOU GOT BOTH EYES OPEN MEBBE YOU NOTICE OWL IS **ET** ALL THE WHOLE STEW?

SO! YOU DECIDED TO EAT **ALL THE WHOLE DING BING** EN-TIRE STEW?

MY **MERE** AN' **ONLY** DESIRE WAS TO **SAVE** YOU THE TROUBLE!

LONG AS YOU WAS SO **THOUGHT- FUL** AN' **SEEIN'** AS YOU IS A **TOP STEW TASTER,** I GONNA WHOP UP A DISH WHAT'LL MAKE YOU FEEL LIKE A **NEW MAN** -----

GOOD FOR ME.

DOES YOU LIKE IT **SWEET?**

NO -- MORE **SOURISH.**

GOOD AN' **SOURY?**

NO, MORE **SALTIER.**

THEN THAT'S **JES' RIGHT** FOR YOU --- G'BYE POGO -

COME AGAIN -- LIKE IN 1956.

GROWF!

141

Chapter 26

HEAR YE, NOW!

Another 65-inning outing.

143

144

145

Chapter 27

CUP YE NOW AN EYE

It pays to think
with your own personal brain.

149

Chapter 28

WEARY, DEARIE

Proves that it is nice
to start the day with at least one beautiful thought,
namely: breakfast.

YOU'S DID IT! YO' LOST VOCAL CHORDS WOULD OF BEEN MOS' HELPFUL IN *ANOTHER* PERFESSION...A PERFESSION JES' CRYIN' FO' YO' ABILITIES --- YOU'D OF BEEN A MILLIONAIRE.

TELL ME MORE.

ALBERT AN' HOUN'DOG IS GONE HAVE A *THINKIN' CONTEST*-- US COULD MANAGE 'EM.

AN' *INSTRUCK* THEM.... I IS *PERSONAL,* AN' *FREEMAN,* THE *BEST THINKER* IN THESE PARTS.

GIVE US A LI'L' SAMPLE...

I THINKS *VERY SCIENTIFIC* AN' METHODICAWOCKLE FOR 'NINSTANCE AT 8 A.M. I THINKS OF A LI'L' *BREAKFAST*--AT TEN I THINKS OF A LI'L' *SNACK*--...

AT *EE*-LEVEN I THINKS OF A LI'L' *MILK* AN' A LI'L' *COOKIE* ---AT *TWELVE* I THINKS OF--UH MM--I THINKS OF A--AT 12 I THINKS ... *WHAT DOES I THINK* OF AT *12?*

UH... HOW 'BOUT A LI'L' *LUNCH?*

THANKEE KINDLY, POGO--US *DON'T MIND IF US DO!* WON'T TAKE A MINUTE TO STEP 'ROUN' TO YO' PLACE.

HOPE YOU'S GOT MACKLE-RONIES.

Chapter *29*

KYRIE COW?

Wherein it is bad luck
to raise a rumpus in the house
unless it is raining.

HOLE A FEW OF THESE THINGS OF POGO'S WHILST I SEARCH OUT A CAN OF BEANS.

WHOO! AFTER ALL THEM YEARS! THE LIGHT OF DAY AGAIN---SAY! WHO WON THE EE-LECTION?

THE GENERAL.

WODDYA KNOW! FINALLY GOT CLEVELAND OUT, HUH?

YEP. THE NEW YORKS WAS TOO MUCH.

THEM YANKEES! WE SHOULD OF MARCHED ON WASHINGTON WHILE McCLELLAN WAS IN CHARGE.

MEBBE SO--- WASHINGTON DIN'T HAVE NO PITCHIN'---

HE WAS A GOOD KID THO--

NEVER TOLE A LIE AN' ALL THAT-- LOOK AT THE TIME 'BOUT THE CHERRY TREE.

HOW KIN I FIND ANY-THING WITH ALL THAT BROUHAHA?

WHO'S THE TALL TOAD WITH THE LOUD GREEN SUNBURN?

JES' FOR THAT YOU KIN GIT OUT.

OH, YEAH--? THIS AIN'T YOUR PLACE-- SALAMANDER, MAKE ME GIT OUT!

I'LL WHITTLE YOU DOWN TO SIZE, BIG TALK.

WHERE'D HE GO? WHERE'D HE GO?

WE COME OVER FOR LUNCH.

WELL, GIT IN LINE.

WE DON'T GOTTA GIT IN LINE, HOUN'DOG... YOU AIN'T IN CHARGE!

OH NO? WE'LL SEE ABOUT THAT!

STOP PUSHIN' MY FRIEND OWL

POGO

COME OUT AN' FIGHT, MOUSE.

MAKE ME, YOU FAT LIZARD.

HEERD TELL THEY WAS A QUALITY FIGHT GOIN' ON AT YO' PLACE---HUSTLED OVER---

YED.. I AIN'T IN IT, THO'.

POGO

MAN--YOU GOT 'EM LOCKED IN YO' PLACE? SOUN' LIKE THEY'S DOIN' A GOOD JOB. ---- WHO'S IN THE CAST?

A LI'L GROUP OF FRIENDS.

MM--LOOKY THERE--- FOR A "PICK-UP" CROWD THEY'S DOIN' JES' FINE!

OWL IS GOOD AT THROWIN' BREAD DOUGH-- AN' HOUN'DOG IS A GREAT MAN WITH GRAVY---

AS USUAL ALBERT GOT A TALENT FOR ROARIN'--BUT WHO'S THE QUICK LI'L CRITTUR WITH THE LONG HANDLED MOLASSES SPOON?

A NEW MOUSE--MORE OR LESS A PRELIM' BOY.

WHAT SPIRIT-- IT ALL MAKES YOU QUIETLY PROUD--

157

H'LO THERE UNCLE POGO AN' H'LO THERE UNCLE PORKYPINE AN' H'LO THERE UNCLE POGO AN' H'LO THERE UNCLE PORKYPINE! WE'S JES' FINE THANKS WE'S JES' FINE THANKS. HOW'S YOU? HOW'S YOU?

HOW IN THE WORL' COME YOU'S PLAYIN' 'ROUND WITH DOUBLE GREETIN'S?

WULL, I AN' GRUNDOON IS TOGETHER ON ACCOUNT I IS BABYSITTIN' OF HIM AN', AS IS WELL KNOWED, HE DON'T TALK GOOD, IF ATALL 'CEPT MEBBE "BYE-BYE" WHICH AIN'T NO GOOD LESSEN YOU IS GOIN' TO MEBBE SAN DIEGO AN' HE AIN'T—

SO YOU IS DOIN' HIS SHARE OF TALKIN' TOO?

YEP, AN' THAT AIN'T ALL! I WAS LEARNIN' HIM GROUNDHOGGIN' TOO— GITTIN' HIM READY TO BE SCAIRT OF HIS SHADOW ··· WATCH NOW BOO, GRUNDOON, BOO!

BUT, AS YOU KIN SEE, HE'S A PUNK STUDY···CAN'T PICK UP THE TRADE ··· NO DOUBT A DISAPPOINTMINT TO HIS FOLKS BUT THAT'S WHAT THEY GITS FOR HAVIN' GROUN'CHUNKS FOR CHILDER. SO LONG UNCLES SO LONG UNCLES!

BYE BYE?

Chapter 30

MOO AND SIX IS PIE

Food for thought
is no substitute for the real thing.

Panel 1: "THE OTHERS HAVE STOPPED FIGHTIN' AN' IS HAVIN' LUNCH....AN' SINCE I AIN'T GOT NOBODY LEFT TO FIGHT WITH, HOW 'BOUT JOININ' 'EM--?" "NOT 'TIL I FINDS THAT MOUSE."

Panel 2: "BUT YOU AN' ME IS SUPPOSED TO BE HAVIN' A CONTEST TO SEE WHO OUT-THINKS THE OTHER--" "THERE HE IS!"

Panel 3: "GOT HIM!"

Panel 4: "HOW ABOUT OUR THINKIN' CONTEST, FRIEND?" "AAARGH! I'LL OUT-THINK YOU WHEN I IS THROUGH OUT-THINKIN' THIS DANG NANG MOUSE!"

Chapter 31

THE SPEAKER SPOKES

It becomes apparent
that thinking is a sucker's game—
You can't take it with you.

ON YO' MARKS! THE SECOND ROUND OF THE GREAT INTER-RATIONAL THINKIN' CONTEST IS AT HAND--- GO IT, CHAPS!

THIS ONE'S ASLEEP

I IS NOT-- AN' EVEN IF I IS-- I KIN OUTDREAM THE BEST THINKIN' HE'S DONE SINCE 19-OUGHT-36.

164

166

Chapter 32

THE REALER WHEELS

From Pop to Peep to Pip

THE THINKIN' CONTEST IS GOIN' ON *REE-LENTLIST!*

PEEP PEEP PEEP PEEP PEEP PEEP

POP POP POP POP POP POP

SO FAR ALBERT IS *THOUSHT* OF 19,206 "PEEPS" BY SPRING BABY FROGS AN' HOUN' DOG IS *THUNK* OF 21,957 "POPS" OF POP CORN.

IT LOOK LIKE *BEAUREGARD'S* BRAIN IS *OVER POWERIN'* ALBERT'S.

NOT *SO* FAST-- ALBERT'S *WAY* OUT FRONT, MY DEAR FELLOW JUDGE, EACH FROG GOT FOUR LIMBS--- *RIGHT?* AN' EACH LIMB GOT FIVE FINGER OR TOE-BONES-- *RIGHT?* SO ALBERT IS THINKIN' MOST *TWENTY-TIMES* FAST AS HOUN' DOG. ANYBODY WITH *HALF-A-EYE* KIN SEE THAT!

AH YES, MY *REVERED COLLEAGUE* -- *IF* YOU LOOKS AT WITH HALF-A-EYE AS IS YO' WON'T-- ACTUAL COUNTIN' 99 GRANNIES OF *SALT* ON EACH LINK OF POP CORN *PLUS BUTTER* SHOW *HOUN' DOG* IS LEADIN' BY A WHISKER AS WIDE AS *MINNESOTA*.

IF THEY GONNA CONTINUE COUNTIN' "PEEPS" AN' "POPS" TO SEE WHO'S OUT-THINKIN' WHO, *I* IS GONE TO WORK.

RIGHT- SOMEBODY BETTER GIT TO *FISHIN'*-- THE COUNTRY'S ECONOMY IS GONE TO POT.

KEEP SCORE FAIR NOW, MY UNBIASED FELLOW JUDGE.

PEEP PEEP PEEP PEEP PEEP

POP POP POP POP POP- HIC! HIC! POP HIC!

DON'T GO COPYIN'.

171

Chapter 33

A KINGDOM FOR A HUM

"Well," murmured one, "let who so make or buy
My clay with long oblivion is gone dry:
But fill me with the old familiar juice,
Methinks I might recover by and by."

OMAR

IF ONE OF *US* IS GONNA BE *THINKIN'* CHAMPEEN, I IS INCLINED TO FAVOR *ME*.

RIGHT THERE YOU PROVES YOU *CAN'T* THINK.

WE BEEN TOGETHER THRU *THICK* AN' *THIN* ~ STARTED OUT *YEARS* AGO... I *REE*-MEMBER *YOU* WHEN *YOU* WAS *BORN* ... A SWEET FACED LITTLE TAD-POLE.

TRUE, TRUE.

WOULD YOU TURN YO' BACK ON *HE WHO* LEARNT YOU TO SNEEZE? *HE WHO* FED YOU? *HE WHO* —

HEY! BEIN' A TURTLE I NEVER *COULD OF BEEN A TAD-POLE* AN' ASIDES I WAS *TWO WEEKS OLD* WHEN *YOU* WAS BORN.

ALL RIGHT! YOU GOT NO RESPECT FOR BYGONES! AT LEAST LET US TRY TO BE *GENTLE-MENS!*

YOU'RE *DOGGONE TOOTIN'! CHOOSE YO' WEAPONS!*

WOOF! WOOF!

ROWF YOP

YIP HOO HA!

WOW

175

Chapter 34

OH, RUBBA DUBBA
DOUBLE DEALS
OH, RUBBA DUBBA DUB

One more last word again.

A NOTE OF THANKS

Someone not long ago, going through POGO's genes like a pocket burglar, decided that the words and music have roots in Joyce, Malthus, Socrates and a lot of other dead people known only to stalwart, quick-striking little bands of thinkers and students who carry with them, in capsule form, the secrets of the human race. These literary Cabots and Lodges, when they speak to their gods, do so in such a welter of erudition that they are fast losing gods and so must take up with comic-strip characters. Well, we are not worth this faith. Give us power and we will turn and destroy. If any innocent, dew-dampened moccasin wearers sneak up on our rear again we will be forced to reveal all. It will be necessary to show there's a touch of the tar brush in us, a bit of the slop along the river, some of the scum that floats in with the tide from another land. This whole crowd is as motley as one man can be. Everything that is here is owed to everybody. If the bomb destroys the human race, the strip will be out of business because our comic sources will have dried up. In this dark, when we all talk at once, some of us must learn to whistle.

WALT KELLY